CONTENTS

M000232561

A | Answer

1 Count the sticks. How many? _____

2 $3 + 6 =$ _____

3 $7 - 2 =$ _____

4 $5p + 2p + 1p =$ _____ p

5 $9p - 6p =$ _____ p

6 $8 = 5 +$ ▢ _____

7 $4 \times 1 =$ _____

8 $5 = 9 -$ ▢ _____

9 $2 + 2 + 2 + 2 =$ _____

10 What time is it? _____ o'clock

B | Answer

1 Find the total number of dots. _____

 and

2 Take 0 from 7. _____

3 Write the word for the missing number.

3, 5, ▢, 9 _____

4 Four more than five _____

5 How many must be taken from 5 to leave 3? _____

6 To eight add zero. _____

7 What number equals double 2? _____

8 From 6 subtract 3. _____

9 Find the difference between 3 and 8. _____

10 Which of these numbers is an odd number?

| 2 | 4 | 5 | 6 | 8 |

_____

C | Answer

1 Write the word for the number that comes between 6 and 8. _____

2 Lucy has 7p and she spends 4p. How much has she left? _____ p

3 Which is the shortest line? A, B or C?

A ——————————

B ————————

C ——————————

_____

4 Jack is 9 years old and Emily is 3 years younger. How old is Emily? _____

5 By how much is 7p more than 3p? _____ p

6 Anu has one 5p and one 2p. How much are these coins worth altogether? _____ p

7 A line is 6cm long. By how many centimetres is it shorter than another line 8cm long? _____ cm

8 Gita has two 2ps and four 1ps. How much money has she altogether? _____ p

9 Which is the third letter in the row?

| A | B | C | D | E | F | G |

_____

10  Daniel gets to school 2 hours later than the time on this clock. At what time does he arrive? _____ o'clock

4

Schofield&Sims

Mental Arithmetic 1

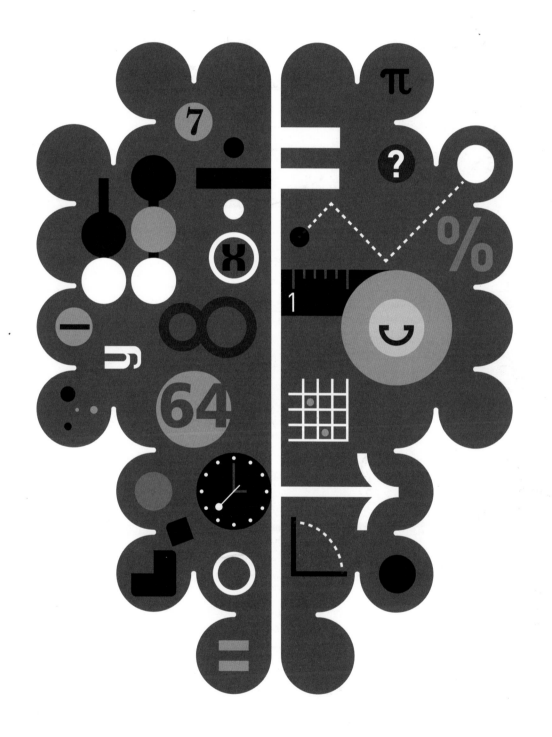

Name

THE LANGUAGE OF MATHS

a.m. when written after ... ... s before midday
Example 9 a.m. m...

brackets if a question has s... ... is in the brackets before
you do the rest of ...
Example in the qu... ...dding 3

denominator the bottom numbe... ...d how many equal parts
something has bee...
Example $\frac{1}{4}$ ← so...

double when you doub... ...ke it twice as big – doubling is the same as multiplying by 2
Example double ... ...because 5 × 2 = 10

dozen another word for 12
Example 'I would like a dozen cakes' means 'I would like 12 cakes'

estimate a sensible guess

even number a whole number that can be divided exactly by two – even numbers always end in 0, 2, 4, 6 or 8
Example 8 divided by 2 = 4, so 8 is an even number

fraction a part of a whole
Example $\frac{1}{2}$ of a doughnut

multiple the multiple of a number can be divided exactly by that number
Example 4, 6, 8 and 100 are all multiples of 2 because 2 divides into them with no remainder

numerator the top number of a fraction – this tells you how many of the parts you have
Example $\frac{2}{3}$ ↖ something has been divided into three equal parts, and you have two of them

odd number a whole number that cannot be divided exactly by two – odd numbers always end in 1, 3, 5, 7 or 9
Example 9 divided by 2 = 4 with 1 left over, so 9 is an odd number

place value the value of a digit depends on where it appears in a number
Example in 40 the '4' is worth 4 tens, but in 4000 the '4' is worth 4 thousands

p.m. when written after a time, 'p.m.' stands for 'post meridian', which means after midday
Example 9 p.m. means 'nine o'clock in the evening'

remainder something left over after a division
Example 9 divided by 2 equals 4 with a remainder of 1

right angle an angle of 90 degrees or 90° (degrees are shown by the symbol °)

A | Answer

1 How many beads? Write the number as a word. _____

○ ○ ○ ○ ○ ○ ○ ○

2 $2 + \square = 8$ _____

3 $4p + 3p + 1p =$ _____ p

4 $9 - 5 =$ _____

5 Which two numbers are missing?

2, $\square$, 4, 5, $\square$, 7, 8 _____ and _____

6 $\square - 3 = 2$ _____

7  What is the time? _____ o'clock

8 $7 + 2 = 2 + \square$ _____

9 $5 - 5 =$ _____

10 $7p = 5p + \square\, p$ _____ p

B | Answer

1 Write the missing even number.

2, 4, $\square$, 8 _____

2 Seven minus four _____

3 Find the total of 3, 0 and 5. _____

4 Take 8 from 8. _____

5 How many days in one week? _____

6 Find the total value of these coins. _____ p

7 Write the number as a word that equals six plus three. _____

8 Add 4p and 5p. _____ p

9 From 9 take 7. _____

10 Subtract 0 from 6. _____

C | Answer

1 Which is the longest line? A, B or C? _____

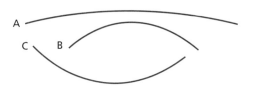

2 Ross spent 3p. He had a 5p left. How much had he at first? _____ p

3 How many days in a school week starting Monday and finishing Friday? _____

4 On a necklace there are nine jewels. Three rubies, three sapphires and the rest are diamonds. How many diamonds are there? _____

5 Jessica has these coins in her purse. She spends 4p. How much has she left? _____ p

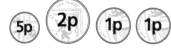

6 Tom is 4 years older than Amy who is 4. How old is Tom? _____

7  This clock is 1 hour slow. What is the correct time? _____ o'clock

8 The length of a line is 8cm. Find the length of a line which is 3cm shorter. _____ cm

9 Katie has 2p and Jakub has twice as much. How much have they altogether? _____ p

10 George has one 5p and two 1ps. How much more does he need to make 9p? _____ p

A

		Answer
1	2 + 5 + 2 =	
2	8 − 0 =	
3	6 + ▢ = 10	
4	3 = 10 − ▢	
5	10 + 7 =	
6	14 − 10 =	
7	5p + 2p + 1p + 2p =	_____ p
8	10p − 8p =	_____ p
9	12 − ▢ = 2	
10	£10 + ▢ = £15	£

B

Answer

1 Write the number 14
   as a word.

2 What is the missing number?

   18, 17, 16, ▢, 14, 13

3 Double 5.

4 Find the total of these notes. £ _____

5 Subtract 6 from 10.

6 What number is added to 9
   to make 19?

7 Find the change from a £10
   note after spending £4.   £ _____

8 Which is the even number?

   | 9 | 11 | 13 | 15 | 16 | 17 |

9 Increase 1 by 10.
   Write the number as a word.

10  What is the
   time after
   3 hours?   _____ o'clock

C

Answer

1 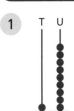 Write the word for the
      number shown on
      the abacus.

2 Olivia spends £3 and £5.
   How much change from
   a £10 note?   £ _____

3 At a party there were 17 plates
   of food. 10 are eaten.
   How many are left?

4 Sophie's cat is 11 years old.
   How old will the cat be in
   6 years' time?

5 What number is taken from
   19 to leave 12?

6 Find the total length of the
   three lines.   _____ cm

   10cm

   7cm

   2cm

7 What is the difference in
   centimetres between the
   longest and shortest lines?   _____ cm

8 If Monday is the first day of the
   week, name the fourth day.

9 How many 2ps have the same
   value as a 10p coin?   _____ 2ps

10 Hassan has two coins in his
   pocket with a total value of
   12p. Name both coins.   _____ p   _____ p

A — Answer

1. 0 + 7 + 0 =

2. 9 + 3 − 5 =

3. 10 + ▨ = 13

4. 2 + 8 =

5. 6 + ▨ = 10

6. ▨ − 5 = 10

7. What comes next?

   4, 8, 12, 16, ▨

8. One 20p = one 10p + ▨ p _____ p

9. 0 + ▨ = 10

10. 10cm + 6cm = _____ cm

B — Answer

1. How many more dots are needed to make eighteen?

   ● ● ● ● ● ● ● ● ● ● ● ●

2. One 20p = one 10p + ▨ 5ps _____ 5ps

3. Write the correct sign, + or −, in place of ●.

   13 ● 4 = 17

4. What number is added to 4 to make 16?

5. Decrease 20 by 5.

6. Which is the eighth letter in the row?

   | A | C | E | G | H | J | M | O | P | W |

7. Find the change from one 10p after spending 7p. _____ p

8. Find the sum of 3, 4, 0 and 10.

9. Ten plus eight minus seven

10. Which is the odd number?

    | 4 | 6 | 12 | 15 | 18 | 20 |

C — Answer

1. Find the total value of these coins. _____ p

2. If the date is 4 May, what is the date 10 days later?

3. The length of a piece of wood is 17cm. How many centimetres are sawn off to leave 10cm? _____ cm

4. Ellie has 5p. Her sister has twice as much. Find the total of their money. _____ p

5. What is the missing number?

   4 + 10 + ▨ = 19

6. I spent 12p, 3p and 4p. How much change did I receive from one 20p? _____ p

7. Sam is 18 years old. How old was he 7 years ago?

8. 16 people were on a bus. Seven got off and three got on. How many people were then on the bus?

9. Which of these shapes is

   a a square   a _____

   b a circle?   b _____

10. On checking his answers to part C of this test, James had three wrong. How many had he correct?

A

		Answer
1	$13 + \square = 18$	
2	$14 - \square = 4$	
3	$18 = 1$ ten $+ \square$ units	
4	$3 + 8 =$	
5	$9p + 4p =$	p
6	$5cm + 7cm =$	cm
7	$12 - 9 =$	
8	$15p - 8p =$	p
9	$11cm - 8cm =$	cm
10	$5 + \square = 13$	

B

Answer

1 What number when added to 10 makes 19?

2 Take 7 from 18.

3 Increase 6 by 5.

4 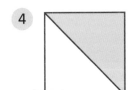 Write the part of the square that is shaded

   a as a word   a _____

   b in digits.   b _____

5 From 13p take 7p. _____ p

6 Find the sum of 6 and 9.

7 17 minus 8

8 6 plus 7

9 What is the difference between 3p and 11p? _____ p

10 Find the total of 7 and the next odd number greater than 7.

C

Answer

1 What is the value of the missing coin? _____ p

$5p + 10p + \bigcirc = 17p$

2 By how many is $8 + 8$ more than 9?

3 The date is 8 June. What is the date one week later?

4 Yasmin has 4p less than her brother who has 13p. How much has Yasmin? _____ p

5 A sandwich is cut into four equal parts. Write the name of each part

   a as a word   a _____

   b in digits.   b _____

6 What is the next even number that is greater than 10?

7 A line is 12cm long. At what measurement is its middle point? _____ cm

8 Matthew has twice as much money as his brother, who has £4. How many pounds have they altogether? £ _____

9  Write in words the time shown on the clock. _____

10 Ali has 18p. He spends 7p and 4p. How much has he left? _____ p

A | Answer

1 2 tens + ▓ units = 20 _____

2 ▓ − 10 = 2 _____

3 7 + 7 = _____

4 3p + 9p = _____ p

5 ▓ + 4 = 19 _____

6 8cm + 6cm = _____ cm

7 13 − 5 = _____

8 What comes next?

8, 16, 24, 32, ▓ _____

9 11cm − 4cm = _____ cm

10 16 − ▓ = 7 _____

B | Answer

1 How many 2ps are worth
two 5ps? _____ 2ps

2 By how many is 6 less than 14? _____

3 What number when added to
8 makes 13? _____

4 Subtract 9p from 18p. _____ p

5 Decrease 12 by 4. _____

6 Add the first three even
numbers. _____

7 Find the difference between
the biggest and smallest of
these amounts of money.

| 9p | 3p | 11p | 7p | 18p |

_____ p

8 8 plus 3 minus 5 _____

9 6 + 7 = 10 + ▓ _____

10 Write the part
of the circle
that is shaded

a as a word   a _____

b in digits.   b _____

C | Answer

1 Sanjay is 8 years old. How old
will he be in 4 years' time? _____

2 Take zero from thirteen. _____

3 Ruby gave two 5ps, two 2ps
and three 1ps to pay for a
pencil. How much did the
pencil cost? _____ p

4 How many half oranges
can be cut from three
whole oranges? _____

5 Write in words the name of
the day of the week that
follows Tuesday. _____

6 How many 2p coins have
the same value as one 5p
and seven 1ps? _____ 2ps

7 There are five men, six women
and eight children on a bus.
How many people are there
in total on the bus? _____

8 Josh has a half and his friend
has a quarter of a cake. What
fraction of the cake is left? _____

9 How many days are there in
a fortnight? _____

10 Write the letters of the
shapes that are triangles.

A

Answer

1. $8 + \boxed{} = 19$ _____

2. $\boxed{} - 7 = 10$ _____

3. 1 ten + $\boxed{}$ units = 14 _____ U

4. $8p + 7p =$ _____ p

5. $2 + 9 =$ _____

6. $14 - 5 =$ _____

7. $3 + 6 = 9 + \boxed{}$ _____

8. $10 - 5 = 12 - \boxed{}$ _____

9. $\frac{1}{2} + \frac{1}{4} =$ _____

10. $6 + 7 = 7 + \boxed{}$ _____

B

Answer

1. What number when added to 4 makes 13? _____

2. 9 is $\boxed{}$ less than 16. _____

3. 18 is $\boxed{}$ more than 9. _____

4. Write the missing word.
   1 whole one = four $\boxed{}$ _____

5. From a dozen subtract 7. _____

6. How much change is left from one 10p after spending two 2ps? _____ p

7. There are 60 minutes in 1 hour. How many minutes in
   a $\frac{1}{2}$h   a _____ min
   b $\frac{1}{4}$h?   b _____ min

8. What odd number is bigger than 11 but less than 15? _____

9. 8 plus 7 minus 10 _____

10. Name the fourth month of the year. _____

C

Answer

1. Which of these lines is the shortest, A, B or C? _____

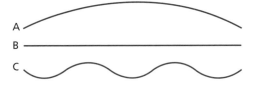

2. Harry is 11 years old. Olivia is three years younger. How old is Olivia? _____

3. Nadeen has nine 1ps. She changes them for three coins. Write the value of each coin. ___ p ___ p ___ p

4. Eva has half a pizza and shares the rest equally between two friends. What fraction does each of her friends have? _____

5. How many children chose crisps as their favourite snack? _____

fruit | ☺ ☺
crisps | ☺ ☺ ☺ ☺
biscuits | ☺ ☺ ☺

one child = ☺

6. Write the correct sign <, > or = in place of ●.
   $3 + 10$ ● $18 - 5$ _____

7. Find the total of one 10p, three 2ps and two 1ps. _____ p

8. Name the month that comes next after December. _____

9. What length is added to 8cm and 6cm to make 20cm? _____ cm

10. Write the name of this shape. _____

A | Answer

1. ☐ + 4 = 17 _____

2. 13 − ☐ = 3 _____

3. 8 + 5 = ☐ + 8 _____

4. 17 = 1 ten + ☐ units _____

5. $\frac{1}{2} - \frac{1}{4}$ = _____

6. 6 + 6 = _____

7. 9p + 8p = _____ p

8. 16cm − 9cm = _____ cm

9. 7 + 5 + 5 = _____

10. 18 − 7 − 6 = _____

B | Answer

1. Write the correct sign <, > or = in place of ●.

   4 + 0 ● 13 − 9 _____

2. Name the eighth month of the year. _____

3. Find the difference between 3cm + 7cm and 19cm. _____ cm

4. 15p is ☐ more than 8p. _____ p

5. Take three-quarters from a whole one. _____

6. What number is 6 less than the sum of 10 and 4? _____

7.  What time is it? Write the answer in digits. _____

8. Find the total of 8p + 5p + 2p. _____ p

9. What number is added to 13 to make 18? _____

10. Find the difference between 17 and the next odd number bigger than 17. _____

C | Answer

1. Add together the even numbers that are less than 8. _____

2. A banana cost 13p. Emma gave two coins to pay for it. If the coins were of different values, what change did she receive? _____ p

3. Estimate (guess) the correct measurement of the line AB. Is it 10cm, 4cm or 8cm? _____ cm

   A _____ B

4. Write < or > to make the statement true.

   48 ☐ 72 _____

5. Ritvick saved 4p and 12p. How much more must he save to have 20p? _____ p

6. Three friends each have a quarter of a chocolate bar. What fraction is left? _____

7. By how much are three 5ps greater than one 10p and two 2ps? _____ p

8. Ahmed had 11 marbles. He lost five and then won 13. How many marbles had he then? _____

9. 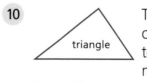 How many square faces does a cube have? _____

10. 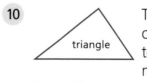 The three sides of a triangle together measure 17cm. Two sides together measure 11cm. Find the length of the third side. _____ cm

A | Answer

1. $8 - 0 + 7 =$ _____

2. Write the word for the missing number.

   0, 10, 20, ■, 40, 50 _____

3. $\frac{1}{4} + \frac{1}{2} + \frac{1}{4} =$ _____

4. $50p = $ ■ $10ps$ _____ 10ps

5. $20p + 40p =$ _____ p

6. $5\frac{1}{2} + \frac{1}{2} =$ _____

7. $50 - 30 =$ _____

8. What number is the arrow pointing to? _____

9. $10cm = 3\frac{1}{2}cm + $ ■ cm _____ cm

10. $2 + 2 + 2 + 2 + 2 + 2 =$ _____

B | Answer

1. Find the total of seven 2ps and one 5p. _____ p

2. Subtract twenty from fifty. _____

3. Write < or > to make this statement true.

   97 ■ 89 _____

4. How much change from two 10ps after spending 12p? _____ p

5. Add 10cm to 40cm. _____ cm

6. Eight groups each of two. How many altogether? _____

7. How many 5ps have the same value as a 20p? _____ 5ps

8. How many days are in January? _____

9. How many twos are there in 12? _____

10. Which three different coins together make 17p? _____ p _____ p _____ p

C | Answer

1. 18 treats are shared equally between two kittens. How many each? _____

2. How long is the line AB? _____ cm

   A ━━━━━━━━━━━━━━━━━━ B

3. Twice seven minus nine _____

4. Sita spends 11p. She gives one 5p and the rest in 2ps. How many 2ps does she give? _____ 2ps

5. If 9 September is on a Monday, on which day is 14 September? _____

6. Martin has 18p. He spends half of it and gives away 2p. How much has he left? _____ p

7. How many children chose science as their favourite subject? _____

   maths   ☺ ☺ ☺

   science ☺ ☺ ☺ ☺ ☺

   history ☺ ☺

   one child = ☺

8. A card costs 8p. Find the cost of two cards. _____ p

9. A box of chocolates contains two layers each of 20 chocolates. How many chocolates are in the box? _____

10. The lengths of two wooden rods are $7\frac{1}{2}cm$ and 10cm. Find the difference in their lengths. _____ cm

Mental Arithmetic 1

A | Answer

1. 6 + 0 + 14 =

2. Write the word for the missing number.

   100, 90, 80, ■, 60

3. 90 − 50 =

4. What comes next?

   24, 32, 40, ■

5. $1\frac{1}{2}$ cm = 10cm − ■ cm _____ cm

6. ■ 2ps = one 20p _____ 2ps

7. $\frac{1}{2}$ cm + $\frac{1}{2}$ cm + $\frac{1}{2}$ cm + $\frac{1}{2}$ cm = _____ cm

8. 100 = 50 + ■

9. 3p + 6p + 7p = _____ p

10. 4 + 4 + 4 + 4 + 4 =

B | Answer

1. Find the total of 5p, 7p and 8p. _____ p

2. Take fifty from eighty. Write the word for the answer.

3. Multiply 4 by 6.

4. $\frac{1}{4}$ of 24

5. By how many pennies is 20p less than nine 10ps? _____ p

6. In which of these months are there 31 days? April, June, August, November.

7. What number is the arrow pointing to?

8. Divide 36 by 4.

9. Write < or > to make the statement true.

   99 ■ 101

10. How many times is 4 added together to make 28?

C | Answer

1. T U Write the word for the number shown on the abacus.

2. By how many centimetres is a line of $13\frac{1}{2}$ cm longer than a line of 8cm? _____ cm

3. Share 20p equally among 4 brothers. How much money do they each receive? _____ p

4. If 6 May is a Tuesday, what is the date on Tuesday a fortnight later?

5. A balloon costs 6p. Find the cost of four balloons. _____ p

6. A coat has 10 buttons. How many coats can be made using 100 buttons?

7. Find the total value of these coins. One 50p, two 10ps and one 20p. _____ p

8. Rosie spends 38p in a shop and gives a 50p in payment. She receives two coins as change. Which coins are they? _____ p _____ p

9. Is this flag pole horizontal or vertical?

10. What is the difference in minutes between the times on these clocks? _____ min

13

SECTION 1 | Test 11

A — Answer

1. Write in words the missing number.

   6, 16, 26, 36, ■, 56 _____

2. Write these numbers in digits.

   a 4 tens 7 units   a _____

   b 6 tens 3 units   b _____

3. 85 + 10 = _____

4. 77 − 10 = _____

5. $1\frac{1}{2} - \frac{1}{4}$ = _____

6. 0 × 4 = _____

7. 8p + 10p + 20p = _____ p

8. 44p = ■ 20ps and ■ p   _____ 20ps and ___ p

9. 16 ÷ 4 = _____

10. 40 = 4 × ■ _____

B — Answer

1. What number is thirteen more than eighty? _____

2. From 20p take 13p. _____ p

3. How many days in February this year? (29 in a leap year) _____

4. Find the total value of these coins. _____ p

5. Write the correct sign +, −, × or ÷ in place of ●.

   6 × 4 = 4 ● 6 _____

6. How much change from two £20 notes after spending £31? £ _____

7. How many halves in six whole ones? _____

8. Decrease 70p by 8p. _____ p

9. What number is 3 times bigger than 4? _____

10. How many days in September? _____

C — Answer

1. Find the difference between the lengths of the rods. _____ cm

2. How many hours from 8.15 a.m. to 12.15 p.m.? _____ hours

3. Write in digits the number that equals 9 tens and 7 units. _____

4. Is this pencil vertical or horizontal? _____

5. The length of a line is 7cm. How long is a line that is 5 times as long as it? _____ cm

6. Which of these numbers is nearest to 60?

   | 58 | 64 | 56 | 61 | 63 | _____

7. What number is the arrow pointing to? _____

8. One-quarter of George's money is 8p. How much has he altogether? _____ p

9. Finlay gave six 5ps to pay for seven sweets at 4p each. How much change did he receive? _____ p

10.
    | Badges |
    | 3 for 20p |

    How many badges can be bought for 60p? _____

A   Answer

1   Write in words the missing number.

   82, 81, 80, ▨, 78   _____

2   Write these numbers in digits.

   a 7 tens 2 units   a _____

   b 5 tens 0 units   b _____

3   58 + 30 =   _____

4   72 − 50 =   _____

5   8 × 4 = 4 × ▨   _____

6   $2 - \frac{3}{4} =$ _____

7   92p = ▨ 10ps and ▨ p   _____ 10ps and ___ p

8   12 halves = ▨ whole ones   _____

9   20 ÷ 4 =   _____

10 Which number is missing from
   the sequence?

   10, 15, 20, ▨, 30, 35, 40   _____

B   Answer

1   Find the sum of 40, 30 and 20. _____

2   Write in words the
       number shown on
       the abacus.   _____

3   How many hours in a day?   _____ h

4   Share 32p equally among
   four children. How much each?   _____ p

5   Increase 50 by 27.   _____

6   Take 32p from two 20ps.   _____ p

7   What number is 5 times
   greater than 8?   _____

8   How many days in November?   _____

9   86 minus 40 plus 20.   _____

10 How many pence is $\frac{3}{4}$ of 12p? _____ p

C   Answer

1   What number is seven less
   than eighty-three?   _____

2   Which of these numbers is
   nearest to 80?

83	75	86	78	84

                                               _____

3   What number is the arrow
   pointing to?

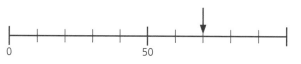

                                               _____

4   How many 5ps are equal
   in value to the sum of
   16p and 14p?   _____ 5ps

5   Find one-quarter of the
   product of 8 and 3.   _____

6   How much change from a
   50p after spending 39p?   _____ p

7   Which sign +, −, × or ÷ is
   used in place of ●?

   10 − 4 = 30 ● 5   _____

8   One half of Marek's money
   is 26p. Find one-quarter of
   his money.   _____ p

9   How many children chose
   blue as their favourite colour? _____

   red   ☺ ☺ ☺

   yellow   ☺ ☺

   blue   ☺ ☺ ☺ ☺

   one child = ☺

10 Find the total length of the
   four sides of the rectangle.   _____ cm

15

PROGRESS TEST 1

Write the numbers 1 to 20 down the side of a sheet of paper.
Write alongside these numbers the **answers only** to the following questions.
Work as quickly as you can. Time allowed – **10 minutes**.

1. $7 + 0 + 9 =$

2. Find the difference between 8 and 15.

3. Nine times $4 =$

4. Divide 45 by 5.

5. Eight tens and 4 units. Write the number in words.

6.  The shape stands for a whole one.
What fraction of it is shaded?

7. After spending 16p and 20p, what change is there out of a 50p?

8. $76 - 40 =$

9. $60 + 33 =$

10. What is the total value of these coins?   5p

11. Four sweets can be bought for 10p. How many sweets for 40p?

12. Write in words the time shown on the clock.

13. $\frac{1}{4}$ of Javed's money is 15p. How much is $\frac{1}{2}$ of his money?

14. The distance all round the square is 28cm.
Find the length of each side.

square

15. There are eight chairs in a row and five rows. How many chairs altogether?

16. How many days in August and September together?

17. Find the sum of $\frac{1}{2}$ of 8p and $\frac{1}{4}$ of 16p.

18. In this sequence which number is incorrect? 0, 5, 10, 15, 20, 25, 30, 34, 40

19. Three lines measure $12\frac{1}{2}$ cm, 3cm and $7\frac{1}{2}$ cm.
By how many centimetres is the shortest line less than the longest line?

20. How many vertices does a cube have?

You will work through Progress Test 1 at **four** different times – once at the end of Section 1, then again after you have completed each of Section 2 Test 4, Test 8 and Test 11.

When you first complete the test:

a colour the first column to show the number of answers correct out of 20

b enter the date.

Each time you take the test, enter the result and the date in the marked columns.

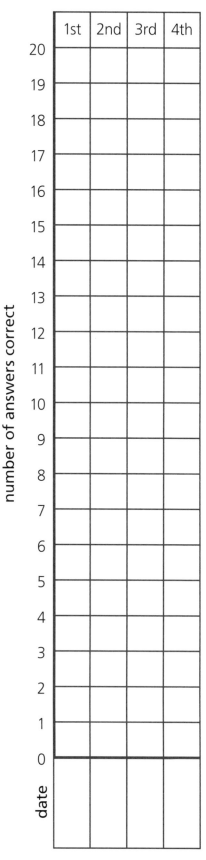

SECTION 2 | Test 1

A | Answer

1. $0 \times 10 =$

2. $15 \div 5 =$

3. $18 + 8 =$

4. $23 - 7 =$

5. A 20p, a 10p and four 2ps = _____ p

6. $7p + 5p + 8p =$ _____ p

7. €20 – €7= € _____

8. $\frac{1}{2} + \frac{1}{2} + \frac{3}{4} + \frac{1}{4} =$

9. $35 = \boxed{} \times 5$

10. $4 \times 8 =$

B | Answer

1. What number is 8 less than 100?

2. Find the total of 27p, 12p and 10p. _____ p

3. How many tens in 90?

4. Write < or > to make the statement true.

    98 $\boxed{}$ 102

5. How many $\frac{1}{2}$ cm in 15cm?

6. Find the difference between 9 and 27.

7. Add the even numbers.

    | 13 | 21 | 8 | 19 | 16 |

8. $(3 \times 10) + \boxed{} = 36$

9. What number is 7 more than 45?

10. Write the two missing numbers in this sequence.

    0, 3, 6, 9, $\boxed{}$, 15, $\boxed{}$

C | Answer

1. Find the total value of these coins. _____ p

2. When 17 is taken from a number the answer is 13. What is the number?

3. One-quarter of the length of a window measures $8\frac{1}{2}$ cm. Find the total length of the window. _____ cm

4. In a class of 32 children 19 were boys. How many were girls?

5.  How many minutes from the time on the clock to half past six? _____ min

6. Five friends win two prizes of 20p which they share equally. How much do they each receive? _____ p

7. What number is the arrow pointing to?

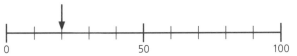

8. Which of these numbers is nearest to 40?

    | 34 | 32 | 42 | 37 | 45 |

9. Which is the cheaper, A or B, and by how much? _____ by ____ p

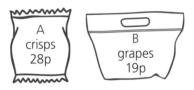

A crisps 28p

B grapes 19p

10. $3 + 3 + 3 + 3 + 3 + 3 = \boxed{} \times 3$ ____ × 3

    $= \boxed{}$

A   Answer

1. $9p + 4p + 7p =$ _____ p

2. $4 \times 3 =$ _____

3. $30 - 12 =$ _____

4. $2\frac{1}{4} =$ ▢ quarters _____

5. $3\overline{)15}$ _____

6. How many days in March? _____

7. $20p - 14p =$ _____ p

8. Five 5ps + three 2ps = _____ p

9. $17 - 4 = 6 +$ ▢ _____

10. $(0 \times 3) + 7 =$ _____

B   Answer

1. Write the two missing numbers in this sequence.

   30, 27, ▢ , ▢ , 18, 15 _____

2. Increase 23p by 8p. _____ p

3. How many days in June and July altogether? _____

4. 7 times 3 _____

5. How much change from a 50p after spending 32p? _____ p

6. How many threes in 27? _____

7. Add the odd numbers.

   | 19 | 12 | 20 | 5 | 8 |

   _____

8. By how many is 24 greater than 17? _____

9. (8×3) minus 10 _____

10. How many quarters in $1\frac{1}{2}$? _____

C   Answer

1. What is the cost of nine pencils at 5p each? _____ p

2. Write the missing number.

   $6 \times 4 =$ ▢ $\times 3$ _____

3. Which three coins together make a total of 62p? ___ p ___ p ___ p

4. Add $\frac{1}{2}$ of 10 to $\frac{3}{4}$ of 8. _____

5. The heights of two cousins are $89\frac{1}{2}$ cm and 94cm. By how many centimetres is one taller than the other? _____ cm

6. Name the month that comes

   a before August   a _____

   b after March.   b _____

7. Samina spends 7p, which is one-quarter of her money. How much had she at first? _____ p

8. Divide 30 by 3 and then add 9. _____

9. Oscar gave six stickers to each of five friends. He had four left. How many had he at first? _____

10. Choose the correct unit of measurement to complete each statement.

    | kilogram | centimetre |
    | litre | gram | metre |

    a The length of Megan's classroom is 10 _____ .

    b Jack's weight is 35 _____ .

    c A jug holds 1 _____ of water.

19

A | Answer

1. $100 - 30 =$

2. $21 \div 3 =$

3. $5 + 5 + 5 + 5 = \boxed{} \times 5 = \boxed{}$ $\underline{} \times 5 =$

4. Nine 2ps + two 5ps =   p

5. $\frac{1}{4}$ of 32 =

6. $10\overline{)80p}$ p

7. $23 + 8 =$

8. $(7 \times 4) + 3 =$

9. $\frac{3}{4} + 1\frac{1}{2} =$

10. Double $(4 \times 3) = \boxed{} \times 3$

B | Answer

1. How many fours in 36?

2. Multiply 10 by 5 and add 6.

3. 1m = 100cm. How many centimetres in $\frac{1}{2}$m?   cm

4. Share 24p equally among three people. How much each?   p

5. What fraction of the strip is not shaded?

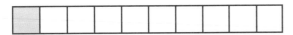

6. By how much is 19p less than three 10ps?   p

7. $34 = (4 \times 10) - \boxed{}$

8. How many minutes from five past six to a quarter to seven?   min

9. How much change from 35p after spending 24p and 7p?   p

10. Write the two missing numbers in this sequence.

    0, 6, 12, $\boxed{}$, 24, $\boxed{}$, 36

C | Answer

1. By how many centimetres is 70cm shorter than 1m?   cm

2. A number multiplied by itself makes 16. What is the number?

3. Divide the total of 4, 6 and 8 by 3.

4. A delivery of potatoes weighs 25kg. How many kilograms have been sold when 17kg are left?   kg

5. How many tenths are there in

   a 2 whole ones   a

   b $\frac{1}{2}$ a whole one?   b

6. How many flat faces does a cylinder have?

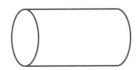

7. There are 50l of water in a bath. 32l are emptied. How many litres are left in the bath?   l

8. By how much is packet A more expensive than packet B?   p

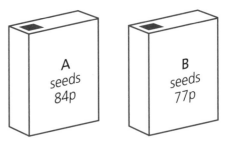

9. What is a quarter of the difference between 36 and 24?

10. $4 + 4 + 4 + 4 = \boxed{} \times 4$ $\times 4$

    $= \boxed{}$

A   **Answer**

1. Fourteen 1ps are worth ▨ 2ps   2ps   2ps

2. $5 \times 6 =$

3. $26 + 9 =$

4. Three 10ps = ▨ 2ps   2ps   2ps

5. $1 - \frac{3}{10} =$

6. $4\overline{)48}$

7. $24kg - 7kg =$ kg

8. $50p - 36p =$ p

9. $1\frac{1}{2}m + 3m + \frac{1}{2}m =$ m

10. $(3 \times 6) + 5 =$

B   **Answer**

1. How many threes in 24?

2. How many pennies are worth two 50ps?   p

3. By how many centimetres is $\frac{1}{2}$m longer than 33cm?   cm

4. What number is 9 less than 22?

5. How many minutes in $1\frac{1}{2}$ hours?   min

6. 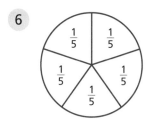 The circle is a whole one. How many fifths in three whole ones?

7. $(0 \times 6) + 8 =$

8. How many days in December?

9. Find the total of 4 times 7p and 2 times 7p.   p

10. If $8 \times 4 = 32$, what is 8×8 equal to?

C   **Answer**

1.  How many vertices does a square-based pyramid have?

2. Write the correct sign >, < or = in place of ●.

    5×6 ● $6 \times 1 \times 5$

3. Jack received 14p change after spending 36p. Which coin did he give the shopkeeper?   p

4. By how many centimetres is $\frac{1}{2}$m greater than $\frac{1}{4}$m?   cm

5. How many 5-litre tins can be filled from 45l of paint?

6. James spent 6p, which was one-tenth of his money. How much money did he have in total?   p

7. Which of these lines is horizontal?

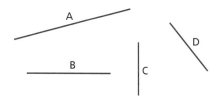

8. A button costs 11p. What change is given from 20p?   p

9. Lily has a £20 note, two £5 notes and a £10 note. She gives £25 to her brother. How much does she have left?   £

10. The product of two numbers is 48. One of the numbers is 6. What is the other?

Schofield & Sims

A | Answer

1. $70 = \blacksquare$ tens _____

2. Write in digits, three hundred. _____

3. $200 + 500 =$ _____

4. $700 - 400 =$ _____

5. $13p + 18p =$ _____ p

6. $\frac{1}{10}$ of 50p = _____ p

7. $25p - 9p =$ _____ p

8. $(2 \times 8) + 5 =$ _____

9. $7 = 28 \div \blacksquare$ _____

10. $16 + 5 - 9 =$ _____

B | Answer

1. Write the missing number in this sequence.

   300, 400, 500, $\blacksquare$, 700 _____

2. Find the total of
   $30p + 6p + 4p + 10p$. _____ p

3. What number is 11 more than 59? _____

4. How many centimetres in 3m? _____ cm

5. How many hours from
   10 a.m. to 2 p.m.? _____ h

6. What fraction of this whole one is shaded? _____

7. By how much is 22p less than three 10ps? _____ p

8. $8 + 8 + 8 + 8 + 8 + 8 + 8 = \blacksquare \times 8$ _____ × 8

   $= \blacksquare$ _____

9. How many quarters in $2\frac{1}{2}$? _____

10. Find the difference between 30 and the sum of 19 and 7. _____

C | Answer

1. Estimate which of the lines X, Y or Z measures 7cm. _____

   X ————————

   Y ——————————————

   Z ——————

2. £1.00 = 100p. How many pence are worth £5.00? _____ p

3. What is the date four days after 29 December? _____

4. Of 35 cars, one-fifth are blue and the rest red.

   How many are red? _____

5. How many 6p stickers can be bought for two 20ps, one 10p and four 1ps? _____

6. By how many centimetres is the length of the rectangle longer than the width? _____ cm

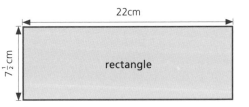

22cm

$7\frac{1}{2}$ cm

rectangle

7. What number when divided by 3 gives 8 for the answer? _____

8. What fraction of these circles is white? _____

9. How much is needed to give eight children 6p each? _____ p

10. $\frac{1}{2}$ kg costs 14p. Find the cost of $1\frac{1}{2}$ kg. _____ p

A — Answer

1. 83p = ▢ 10ps and ▢ 1ps — _____ 10ps and _____ 1ps

2. Write in digits, four hundred and eighty.

3. 250 + 100 =

4. 720 – 100 =

5. One-third of 27p = _____ p

6. 21 – 5 – 7 =

7. 30 – 3 = 40 – ▢

8. 10 × 2 = ▢ × 4

9. Six 2ps + 3p = ▢ 5ps — _____ 5ps

10. 48 ÷ 8 =

B — Answer

1. What number is halfway between 50 and 100?

2. Write the missing number in this sequence.
   490, 590, 690, ▢, 890

3. One-tenth of a line measures $5\frac{1}{2}$ cm. Find the total length. _____ cm

4.  Write in words the time that is 1h and 40min later.

5. How many 10ps in £1.00?

6. Find the difference between $\frac{3}{4}$ and 2.

7. How many metres is 600cm? _____ m

8. Divide 27 into three equal parts. Find one part.

9. Find the total of 300, 150 and 500.

10. Multiply 8 by 5 and then add 3.

C — Answer

1. A number minus 7 equals 19. What is the number?

2. By how many pence is £1.38 more than £1.00? _____ p

3. The rectangle is twice as long as it is wide. Find the width. _____ cm

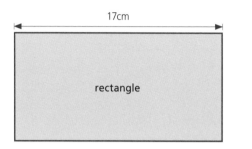
17cm

rectangle

4. Two notes together make £40. What are the notes? £ _____ £ _____

5. What number is the arrow pointing to? _____

0   100

6. Ali has these coins. How much has he altogether? _____ p

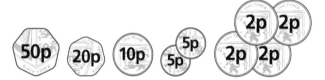
50p 20p 10p 5p 5p 2p 2p 2p 2p

7. How many days are there from 28 May to 4 June? (Do not count 28 May.)

8. A bucket, when a quarter full, holds $3\frac{1}{2}$ l. How many litres will it hold when three-quarters full? _____ l

9. Three breadsticks cost 12p. How much is paid for four breadsticks? _____ p

10. Which of these lengths is nearest to 60cm?
    $\frac{1}{2}$ m, $62\frac{1}{2}$ cm, $58\frac{1}{2}$ cm, 66cm _____ cm

A | Answer

1. 77 + 30 =

2. Write in words the number 203.

3. 450 + 300 =

4. 890 − 500 =

5. 8)‾2‾4‾

6. £1.25 = £1 + ☐ pennies

7. 23 − ☐ = 17

8. What comes next?

    45, 85, 125, 165, ☐

9. 7 × ☐ = 21

10. 40 + 6 = 30 + ☐

B | Answer

1. Find the sum of £1.00 and 45p.

    £

2. How many centimetres in 5m?

    cm

3. Complete this sequence.

    310, 210, 110, ☐

4. Take 40 from 200.

5. Add the odd numbers between 16 and 20.

6. How many hours from 11 a.m. to midnight?

    h

7. Find the change from £1 after spending 85p.

    p

8. How many times 30 is 300?

9. What is the difference between a whole one and three-tenths?

10. 9 + 7 = 20 − ☐

C | Answer

1. £1 is worth one 50p and some 5ps. How many 5ps?

    5ps

2. What number is 10 more than 490?

3. The lengths of four lines are $8\frac{1}{2}$cm, $4\frac{1}{2}$cm, 17cm, 24cm. Find the difference between the shortest and the longest lines.

    cm

4.  The time on this clock is 20 minutes slow. Write the correct time in words.

5. 48p is divided equally among six children. How much each?

    p

6. There are four glasses of juice in a litre. How many litres are needed to give 36 children a glass each?

    l

7. By how much is $\frac{1}{3}$ of 30p greater than $\frac{1}{5}$ of 30p?

    p

8. ● stands for a missing sign, +, −, × or ÷.

    8 × 0 = 4 ● 4

    What is the correct sign?

9. Sasmita buys two sweets at 7p each. How much change out of a 50p does she receive?

    p

10. Write in words the number shown on this abacus.

A   Answer

1   400 + 20 + 6 =

2   £0.72 = ▩ p   p

3   40 ÷ 8 =

4   5 × 3 × 0 =

5   1m 38cm = ▩ cm   cm

6   97 − 50 =

7   13 quarters = ▩

8   4p + ▩ p = one 20p   p

9   100 − 20 =

10   18 ÷ 3 =

B   Answer

1   How many tens are there in 380?

2   What number is one more than 499?

3   By how many centimetres is 1m 55cm longer than 1m?   cm

4   How many 2ps are worth one 50p?   2ps

5   Share nine times 5p equally among five girls. How many pennies each?   p

6   £1.00 = ▩ 20ps   20ps

7   How many minutes from twenty to 12 until half past 12?   min

8   $1\frac{1}{2}$ = ▩ tenths

9   What is the value of the 5 in the number 542?

10   Write the next number in this sequence.

     133, 123, 113, 103, ▩

C   Answer

1   What number is the arrow pointing to?

2   Rearrange the digits 6, 9, 8 to make the largest possible number.

3   What fraction of this shape is shaded?

4   Write as £s this sum of money. £3 and 27p.   £

5   A piece of wood is 18cm shorter than 1m. How long is the piece of wood?   cm

6   On a trip Ellie pays half fare, which is £8. How much is the total fare for Ellie and her mother?   £

7   How many children chose red as their favourite colour?

red   ☺ ☺ ☺

yellow   ☺ ☺ ☺ ☺

blue   ☺

one child = ☺

8   Tom bought a toy for 68p. How much change did he receive from £1?   p

9   $\frac{1}{3}$ of a sum of money is 12p. How much is $\frac{2}{3}$ of the money?   p

10   Each centimetre on this line stands for 8m. What length in metres does the line stand for?   m

     cm

A — Answer

1 29 + 7 =

2 25 – 6 =

3 600 + 70 + 6 =

4 145cm = ▪ m ▪ cm   m   cm

5 9 × 2 = ▪ × 6

6 $1\frac{1}{2} - \frac{3}{4} =$

7 How many days in June?

8 £0.14 = ▪ p   p

9 96 ÷ 8 =

10 (7 × 4) + 3 =

B — Answer

1 Add together 3p, 6p and 14p.   p

2 6 × 8 = ▪ tens ▪ units   T   U

3 By how many centimetres is $\frac{1}{2}$ m longer than 38cm?   cm

4 Find the missing numbers.
   329 = ▪ tens ▪ units   T   U

5 Increase £1.07 by 3p.   £

6 What number is 20 less than 600?

7 Complete this sequence.
   $\frac{1}{3}, \frac{2}{3}, 1, 1\frac{1}{3}, 1\frac{2}{3}$, ▪

8 Share 28p equally among four people.   p

9 How many minutes from five to nine a.m. to twenty past nine a.m.?   min

10 £1.00 is worth four 20ps and ▪ p.   p

C — Answer

1 Jo has five bank notes of the same value. She has £100. What value is each note?   £

2 Which coin has the same value as £0.05?   p

3 What number when divided by 3 gives 9 for the answer?

4 By how many kilograms is bag A heavier than bag B?   kg

A 27kg

B 9kg

5 132 children each give 1p to the school fund. Write the total as £s.   £

6 At what measurement is the middle point of a line of this length?   cm

25cm

7 By how much is 95p less than £1.05?   p

8 If the date of the first Monday in January is the 6th, what is the date of the fourth Monday in the month?

9 Which of these parts of a cake is the largest?
   $\frac{1}{4}, \frac{1}{2}$ or $\frac{1}{3}$

10 This is a row of stamps. How many are there in a sheet of eight rows?

A | Answer

1. 24 − 8 = _____

2. 3 + 39 = _____

3. (6 × 8) + 4 = _____

4. 700 + 40 + 2 = _____

5. 1m 44cm = ▢ cm _____ cm

6. 10 × 4 = 8 × ▢ _____

7. £1.00 + 6p = £ _____

8. Three-quarters of 1 hour = ▢ minutes _____ min

9. 24 ÷ ▢ = 8 _____

10. 5 × 0 = 6 − ▢ _____

B | Answer

1. How many tens in 400? _____

2. Divide 42 into 6 equal parts. Find one part. _____

3. Find the product of 9 and 4. _____

4. From £1.00 take 12p. _____ p

5. What number is 10 more than 192? _____

6. One 50p + ▢ 5ps = £1.00 _____ 5ps

7. Complete the sequence.
   115, 110, 105, 100, ▢ _____

8. By how many centimetres is $\frac{1}{2}$m longer than 26cm? _____ cm

9. Write in words the time that is three-quarters of an hour after ten to eight in the evening.
   _____

10. What is the value of the digit underlined in the number 3<u>6</u>7? _____

C | Answer

1. In a class there were 26 children. Eight of them were girls. How many were boys? _____

2. Which of these lines is vertical? _____

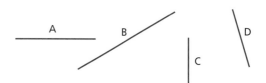

3. By how much is the largest of these sums of money greater than the smallest?

   | £0.96 £1.10 £0.98 £1.07 | _____ p

4. Write the name of the shape that is the flat face of a cone. _____

5. Name the month of the year that comes before August. _____

6. How many 5ps must be added to 80p to make £1.00? _____ 5ps

7. 20 people can travel on a minibus. How many buses are needed to carry 100 people? _____

8. What is the cost of $1\frac{1}{2}$m of material at 18p per metre? _____ p

9. Shenaz has one 50p and eight 1ps in her purse. She spends 39p. How much has she left? _____ p

10. The triangle has three equal sides. The total length of the sides is 12cm. What is the length of one side? _____ cm

triangle

A | Answer

1 300 + 20 + 7 = _____

2 (6 × 3) + 2 = _____

3 24 ÷ ■ = 4 _____

4 1m 9cm = ■ cm _____ cm

5 $\frac{1}{3}$ of 21p = _____ p

6 209 = ■ tens 9 units _____ T

7 Write as £s: two pounds 20 pence. £ _____

8 106 − 20 = _____

9 $\frac{1}{2}$ hour + 15min = ■ min _____ min

10 £1.00 − 16p = _____ p

B | Answer

1 Complete this sequence.

   407, 307, 207, 107, ■ _____

2 Find the total of 19, 7 and 5. _____

3 How many centimetres in $2\frac{1}{2}$m? _____ cm

4  How many minutes to the next hour? _____ min

5 By how much is 76p greater than 50p? _____ p

6 202 = (20 × ■) + 2 _____

7 Add four to zero times five. _____

8 What must be added to 86p to make £1.00? _____ p

9 How many $\frac{1}{2}$kg in 8kg? _____

10 68p = five 10ps + ■ 2ps _____ 2ps

C | Answer

1 60 chairs are arranged in rows of 10. How many rows? _____

2 Kieran spent 10p and 8p. He had 5p left. How much had he at first? _____ p

3 If the line AB is 27cm long and the line AC is 18cm long, how long is CB? _____ cm

4 Which two of these sums of money when added together make 40p?

   | 11p 12p 19p 28p |

   _____ p _____ p

5 The difference between two numbers is 9. The smaller number is 18. What is the larger number? _____

6 $\frac{3}{4}$ of Chloe's money is 27p. What is $\frac{1}{4}$ of her money? _____ p

7 A shop closes from half past 12 p.m. until 2 p.m. For how many hours and minutes is the shop closed? _____ h _____ min

8 Find the cost of 2kg of potatoes at 20p per $\frac{1}{2}$kg. _____ p

9 What number when multiplied by 5 will give a product of 100? _____

10 A carton of milk costs 48p. Faye pays with an equal number of 5ps and 1ps. How many of each coin does she use? _____

A | Answer

1 Write in digits the number five hundred and seven. _____

2 194 + 8 = _____

3 $\frac{1}{8}$ of 24p = _____ p

4 403cm = ☐ m ☐ cm _____ m _____ cm

5 700 – 90 = _____

6 £1.54 = ☐ p _____ p

7 (4 × 8) + 5 = _____

8 How many days in March? _____

9 One 50p + three 10ps + two 2ps = _____ p

10 10 × 10 × 10 = _____

B | Answer

1 What number must be added to 52 to make 70? _____

2 To £1.06 add 40p. £ _____

3 From £1.58 take 16p. £ _____

4 Increase $8\frac{1}{2}$ cm five times. _____ cm

5 Write < or > to make the statement true.

   479 ☐ 481 _____

6 How many quarters in $5\frac{1}{2}$? _____

7 Complete this sequence.

   94, 96, 98, 100, ☐ _____

8 Name the month that is three months after November. _____

9 How many hundreds in 1000? _____

10 Share 36p equally among four friends. How much each? _____ p

C | Answer

1 Which two of these sums of money when added together make 50p?

   | 13p 18p 27p 32p | _____ p _____ p

2 How many times is the 5 in 51 greater than the 5 in 15? _____

3 A petrol tank, which holds 60l, is $\frac{3}{4}$ full. How many more litres will it take? _____ l

4  The total length of the four sides of the square is 38cm. Find the length of one side. _____ cm

5 A TV programme starts at quarter to six and ends 35min later. Write in words the time it finishes. _____

6 What number is the arrow pointing to? _____

   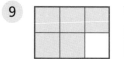
   0   100

7 Which of these amounts of money is nearest to £1.00?

   | £1.10 95p £0.98 £1.05 | £ _____

8 Three numbers when added together total 639. One number is 9 and another is 600. Find the third. _____

9 What fraction of the shape is shaded? _____

10 Five biscuits cost 25p. How much is paid for two biscuits? _____ p

Write the numbers 1 to 20 down the side of a sheet of paper.
Write alongside these numbers the **answers only** to the following questions.
Work as quickly as you can. Time allowed – **10 minutes**.

1 7 + ▢ = 15

2 23 minus 9 =

3 There are four apples in a bag. How many apples are there in six bags?

4 Share 20p and two 2ps equally among four people. How much each?

5 There are 10 stamps in a row. How many stamps are there in a sheet of 10 rows?

6 Write in digits the sum of five hundreds, seven tens and three units.

7 What number is 5 more than 199?

8 Take 7 from 403.

9 How many days in September and October put together?

10 How many 10p coins are given in exchange for £3.60?

11 $\frac{1}{8}$ of the length of a piece of wood measures 9cm. What is its whole length?

12 The time shown on a clock is five past eight but it is 20 minutes fast.
Write the correct time.

13 Find in £s the total value of these coins.

14 How much change from £1 after buying a plum for 12p and an apple for 27p?

15 A parcel has a mass of 25kg. Another parcel is $6\frac{1}{2}$kg lighter.
Find the mass of this parcel.

16 A length of cloth measures 208cm. Write this length in metres and centimetres.

17 Find the total number of days in the last two months of the year.

18 James puts nine books in each of five boxes. He has four books left.
How many has he altogether?

19 An ice lolly costs 34p. Find the cost of three lollies.

20

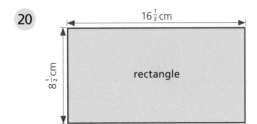

Find in centimetres the distance all round the rectangle.

PROGRESS TEST 2 | Results Chart

You will work through Progress Test 2 at **four** different times – once at the end of Section 2, then again after you have completed each of Section 3 Test 4, Test 8 and Test 12.

When you first complete the test:

a colour the first column to show the number of answers correct out of 20

b enter the date.

Each time you take the test, enter the result and the date in the marked columns.

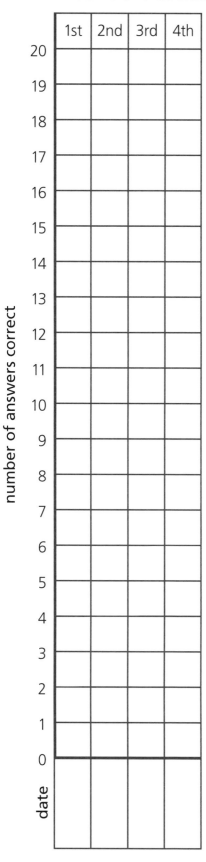

A

Answer

1 H T U What is the number shown on the abacus? _____

2 13 + 9 = _____

3 31 − 4 = _____

4 8 + 8 + 8 + 8 + 8 = _____ ☐ × 8 = ☐   × 8 = _____

5 24 ÷ 4 = _____

6 £1.37 = £1 and ☐ p _____ p

7 307cm = ☐ m ☐ cm _____ m _____ cm

8 $1\frac{1}{2}$h = ☐ min _____ min

9 56 ÷ 8 = _____

10 Four 5ps and nine 2ps = _____ p

B

Answer

1 What is the missing number?
582 = 500 + ☐ + 2 _____

2 Increase 95p by 15p = £ ☐   £ _____

3 What number is 7 less than 204? _____

4 Georgia is watching TV at half past four in the afternoon. Is this time a.m. or p.m.? _____

5 How much change out of 20p after spending 8p? _____ p

6 How many 5ps are worth three 10ps and five 2ps? _____

7 A piece of wood is cut into three equal parts. What fraction of the whole is each part? _____

8 Find the difference between the longest and shortest of these lengths.

$9\frac{1}{2}$cm 26 cm $18\frac{1}{2}$cm $30\frac{1}{2}$cm

_____ cm

9 How many whole ones in 20 quarters? _____

10 10 × ☐ p = £1.70 _____ p

C

Answer

1 What number is added to 409 to make 449? _____

2 Sam has 6p and Abi has 14p more. How much have they altogether? _____ p

3 Monday is 30 April. What is the date on the next Thursday? _____

4 Which of these weights is nearest to 20kg?

19kg $20\frac{1}{2}$kg 14kg 22kg

_____ kg

5 How much has Preeti spent if she has 11p change out of a 50p? _____ p

6 Find the length of the line CB. _____ cm

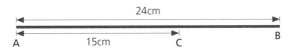

7 Jess has saved eight 10ps. How much more must she save to buy a magazine costing £1.25? _____ p

8 Which of these numbers is a multiple of 4?

14 18 22 24

_____

9 Eight balloons cost 56p. Find the cost of one balloon. _____ p

10 The picture shows a layer of doughnuts in a box. How many doughnuts are in a box of four layers? _____

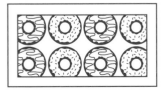

A   **Answer**

1 Write the number shown on the abacus.

2   75 + 8 =

3   63 − 7 =

4   9 × 4 = 4 × ☐ = ☐

5   3 weeks = ☐ days

6   2m 40cm = ☐ cm   cm

7   (8 × 0) + 5 =

8   36 ÷ 3 =

9   Three pounds 29p = £ ☐   £

10 One thousand = 100 × ☐

B   **Answer**

1   What number is 300 less than 780?

2   Decrease £1.15 by 20p.   p

3   Find the total of 8p, 9p and 10p.   p

4   How many fives are there in 500?

5   Write in words the time $\frac{1}{4}$ hour after ten to 11.

6   What is $\frac{3}{4}$ of 16?

7   Find the missing sum of money.

     ☐ p ÷ 5 = 7p   p

8   How many 5ps have the same value as two 20ps and five 2ps?   5ps

9   Divide a length of 36cm into six equal parts. What is the length of each part?   cm

10 Take 37cm from $\frac{1}{2}$ metre. How many centimetres are left?   cm

C   **Answer**

1   This cube is standing on a table. How many of its edges are vertical?

2   What number is taken from 376 to leave 306?

3   Which of these fractions is

    a the largest   a

    b the smallest?   b

$\frac{1}{3}$	$\frac{1}{2}$	$\frac{1}{4}$	$\frac{1}{10}$

4   The time on Joseph's watch is five past 3 but the correct time is ten to 3. Is his watch fast or slow and by how many minutes?   by   min

5   In a collection there were 309 1ps. Write this amount as £s.   £

6   Which of these numbers is a multiple of 3?

28	20	16	12

7   What number when multiplied by itself gives 25 as the answer?

8   One-third of Ben's money is 9p.

    a What value is $\frac{2}{3}$ of his money?   a   p

    b How much money does he have in total?   b   p

9   Isla received 15p change after spending 35p. Which coin did she use to pay?   p

10 How many children chose monkeys as their favourite animal?

    tiger | ☺

    giraffe | ☺ ☺ ☺

    monkey | ☺ ☺

    ☺ = two children

A · Answer

1. Write this number in digits.
   Seven hundred and eleven _____

2. 29 + 40 = _____

3. 81 − 30 = _____

4. 513 = ▨ tens 3 units _____ T

5. 3 × 3 × 3 = _____

6. $\frac{1}{10}$ of 90p = _____ p

7. £1.00 = one 50p + ▨ 2ps _____ 2ps

8. 3m 20cm = ▨ cm _____ cm

9. How many days in October? _____

10. 72 ÷ 8 = _____

B · Answer

1. What number is 8 more
   than 493? _____

2. From 20 take the product
   of 4 and 5. _____

3. Write the correct sign +, −,
   × or ÷ in place of ●.
   13 − 7 = 12 ● 2 _____

4.  This clock is
   1 hour fast.
   Write in
   words the real
   time and use
   a.m. or p.m.

   afternoon _____

5. By how much is 7p less
   than 19p? _____ p

6. Find the total of £1.20
   and £1.80. £ _____

7. $3 - \frac{1}{4} - \frac{1}{2} =$ _____

8. Write the missing number
   in this sequence.
   350, 300, 250, 200, ▨, 100 _____

9. What is the sum of 325g
   and 50g? _____ g

10. How many days in May, June
    and July in total? _____

C · Answer

1. What is the value of the 4
   in the number 648? _____

2. Carrots cost 70p per kg.
   How much would $1\frac{1}{2}$ kg cost? £ _____

3. What number is two hundred
   more than 707? _____

4. | Pens |
   | 3 for 20p |

   How many pens
   are bought
   for 80p? _____

5. Which of these numbers
   is a multiple of 8?

   | 73 85 56 50 59 |

   _____

6. Emily moves house on
   10 February and Dan moves
   house on 10 November.
   How many months earlier than
   Dan does Emily move house? _____

7. 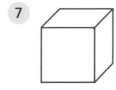 This cube is standing
   on a table.
   How many of
   its edges are
   horizontal? _____

8. Priya saves one 20p each
   month. How much does she
   save in one year? £ _____

9. $\frac{1}{2}$ of a sum of money is
   £1.40. What is $\frac{1}{4}$ of the
   money? _____ p

10. 10 of these circles are placed
    side by side, as shown in
    the picture. What is the
    total length? _____ cm

    $3\frac{1}{2}$ cm $3\frac{1}{2}$ cm $3\frac{1}{2}$ cm

A

		Answer
1	Write this number in words. 500 + 9	_____
2	50 + 48 =	_____
3	70 – 29 =	_____
4	239 = ▨ hundreds ▨ units	H _____ U _____
5	(8 × 1) + 5 =	_____
6	$\frac{1}{5}$ of 35p =	_____ p
7	£1.00 = nine 10ps and ▨ 2ps	_____ 2ps
8	500cm = ▨ m	_____ m
9	1h 20min + ▨ min = 2h	_____ min
10	32 ÷ 4 =	_____

B

		Answer
1	What number is 10 less than 1000?	_____
2	Find the difference between $1\frac{3}{4}$ and 3.	_____
3	What number is equal to (9 × 8) + 3?	_____
4	Find the change from three 10ps after spending 18p and 6p.	_____ p
5	From £1.30 take 50p.	_____ p
6	By how many centimetres is 405cm greater than 4m?	_____ cm
7	What is the missing number? ▨ × 8 = 96	_____
8	Find the total value of these coins.	_____ p

9	2 × 2 × 2 × 2 =	_____
10	1000g = 1kg. How many grams is $\frac{1}{2}$ kg?	_____ g

C

		Answer
1	In a bag there are nine 1ps and the same number of 2ps. How much are all the coins worth?	_____ p
2	Some peaches were cut into quarters. There were then 40 pieces. How many peaches were cut?	_____
3	505 people were at a concert. 200 were men, 200 were women and the rest children. How many children were there?	_____
4	4kg of dog food costs 48p. Find the price per kilogram.	_____ p
5	This bar of chocolate is divided into squares. How many squares of chocolate are there in two bars?	_____

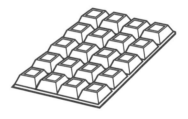

6	Mia measures 142cm in height. By how many centimetres is she taller than 1m?	_____ cm
7	Louis gets on the bus at twenty to four. He arrives home at quarter past four. How many minutes does the journey take?	_____ min
8	Which of these numbers is a multiple of 5? 23 40 17 34 53	_____
9	Write < or > to make this statement true. (500 – 30) ▨ 472	_____
10	Which of these shapes, A, B, C or D, is a rectangle?	

A   Answer

1. $200 + 300 + 72 =$ _____

2. One thousand = $(4 \times 100) +$ ▢ _____

3. $4 \times 10 = 5 \times$ ▢ _____

4. $17 - 9 = 12 -$ ▢ _____

5. £0.37 = ▢ p _____ p

6. How many grams in $1\frac{1}{2}$ kg? _____ g

7. $26 + 13 + 7 =$ _____

8. $24 \div 8 = 12 \div$ ▢ _____

9. Twice $6\frac{1}{4}$ l = _____ l

10. $\frac{1}{10}$ kg = ▢ g _____ g

B   Answer

1. What number is added to 306 to make 366? _____

2. Double 9 and then add 7. _____

3. By how much is 82p less than £1.00? _____ p

4. What fraction of 1kg is 200g? _____

5.  How many minutes from the time on the clock to half past 5? _____ min

6. Find the total length of 27cm, 40cm and 8cm. _____ cm

7. Write the name of the sixth month in the year. _____

8. By how many pence are five 5ps less than four 10ps? _____ p

9. How many times can a length of 8cm be cut from 64cm? _____

10. Which of these numbers is nearest to 50?
45	56	43	58

C   Answer

1. 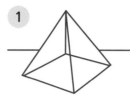 This picture shows a square-based pyramid standing on a table. How many of its edges are horizontal? _____

2. Which two of these sums of money when added together make 20p?
6p	9p	8p	14p
   _____ p _____ p

3. 1kg of cheese costs £7.80. Find the cost of one-tenth of 1kg. _____ p

4. The number 27 is a multiple of which of these numbers? _____
6	5	4	3

5. Darcy saves 10p each day for a fortnight. Find her total savings. £ _____

6. Guess (estimate) which of these lines, X, Y or Z, measures 5cm. _____

   X ———————————————

   Y ———————————————

   Z ——————————

7.  Sara loses four of these hairclips. What fraction of all the hairclips has she lost? _____

8. How many hours and minutes after midday is the time on the clock? _____ h _____ min

9. What number is the arrow pointing to? _____

   0   1000

10. Matthew has these coins. How much more must he save to have £1.00? _____ p

A · Answer

1. H T U Write in words the number shown on the abacus.

2. 40 + 30 + 7 =

3. (8 × 4) − 12 =

4. $\frac{1}{10}$ of five hundred =

5. 19 − 6 = 7 + ▢

6. $\frac{1}{3}$ of six 10ps = ▢ p _____ p

7. 90 − 40 − 3 =

8. 204 = ▢ tens ▢ units _____ T ____ U

9. 7 × 8 × 0 =

10. 1kg − 200g = ▢ g _____ g

B · Answer

1. Rearrange the digits 7, 3, 5 to make the smallest possible number.

2. Find the number that is thirty more than four times zero.

3. Share £1.50 equally among 10 people. How much each? _____ p

4. Find the difference between 700g and 1kg. _____ g

5. What fraction of the shape is shaded?

6. How many minutes are there from quarter past twelve to one o'clock? _____ min

7. 5p plus three 2ps plus four 5ps _____ p

8. Find the change from 30p after spending 12p and 9p. _____ p

9. 10 × 4 × 10 =

10. 1 litre (l) = 1000 millilitres (ml). How many millilitres in $\frac{1}{2}$ litre? _____ ml

C · Answer

1. A daily newspaper costs 30p. How much is paid for the days Monday to Saturday? £ _____

2. How many $\frac{1}{2}$ l bottles can be filled from 8l of water?

3. RAFFLE TICKET
   number
   390
   50p
   What is the number on the raffle ticket when 20 more have been sold?

4. How much would be paid for the 20 tickets? £ _____

5. There are 30 dogs in a park. $\frac{2}{3}$ of them are brown. How many is that?

6. On this line 1cm stands for 5m. How many metres does the whole line stand for? _____ m

   cm

7. Six friends shared a prize equally. They each received 8p and there were two 1ps left. What was the value of the prize? _____ p

8. Alfie is 1m 35cm tall and Sofia is 142cm tall. By how many centimetres is Sofia taller than Alfie? _____ cm

9. A notebook and pencil cost 70p. The pencil cost 11p. How much did the notebook cost? _____ p

10. square
    A square has
    a ▢ equal sides a _____
    b ▢ right angles. b _____

A | Answer

1. Write in words the number that is the same as 40 tens. _____

2. $19 + 17 + 1 =$ _____

3. $65 - 35 =$ _____

4. $16p \times 2 =$ _____ p

5. $8\overline{)56}$ _____

6. 1m – 40cm = ▮ cm _____ cm

7. 40p + £2.00 = £ ▮ £ _____

8. $3 \times 1\frac{1}{4} =$ _____

9. $100 + 60 + 50 =$ _____

10. $\frac{1}{5}$ of 1kg = ▮ g _____ g

B | Answer

1. Find the sum of 480 and 30. _____

2. $9 + 8 =$ ▮ $+ 10$. What is the value of the missing number? _____

3. How many months are there from 30 April to 30 November? _____

4. From 2m take 45cm. _____ m _____ cm

5. How many 2ps are changed for five 10ps? _____ 2ps

6.  What is the time 3 hours later than the time on the clock? _____

7. By how many grams is 380g less than $\frac{1}{2}$ kg? _____ g

8. Which of these lengths is nearest to $\frac{1}{2}$ m? _____ cm

   | $48\frac{1}{2}$cm | 53cm | 46cm | 51cm |

9. Find the total of 25p and £1.80. £ _____

10. One-third of 24l _____ l

C | Answer

1. 180 party invitations are put into packets of 10. How many packets? _____

2. Which of these numbers is a multiple of both 5 and 10? _____

   | 35 | 15 | 46 | 25 | 90 |

3. 28 March is the first day of a holiday which ends on 5 April. How many days? _____

4. A lemon costs 11p. How many lemons can be bought for six 10ps and three 2ps? _____

5.  All the pencils are shared equally among three children. How many pencils each? _____

6. How many children chose running as their favourite sport? _____

   swimming | ☺
   running | ☺ ☺ ☺   ☺ = 5 children
   football | ☺ ☺

7. How many packets can be filled from 1kg of cereal? _____

8. By how many is $\frac{1}{10}$ of 70 less than $\frac{1}{4}$ of 80? _____

9. Holly gave £1 to pay for her magazine. She received in change one 2p, six 1ps and one 5p. Find the cost of the magazine. _____ p

10. Which of these angles, A, B, C or D, is a right angle? _____

A | Answer

1. 20 + 80 + 30 + 4 = _____

2. Write in words the number that equals 15 tens and three.
_____

3. 100 – 76 = _____

4. (4 × 8) + 5 = _____

5. 20p – 11p = _____ p

6. 44 ÷ 4 = _____

7. $\frac{1}{2}$ of $3\frac{1}{2}$ kg = _____ kg

8. 68p = three 20ps + ▢ 2ps _____ 2ps

9. 5 + 9 + 7 = 9 + ▢ + 5 _____

10. £1.46 – 90p = ▢ p _____ p

B | Answer

1. What number is equal to the sum of 10 tens and 18? _____

2. Multiply by 6 the difference between 13 and 8. _____

3. What is the next even number that is greater than 48? _____

4. Find the cost of $1\frac{1}{2}$ kg at 90p per $\frac{1}{2}$ kg. £ _____

5.  What fraction of this shape is shaded? _____

6. By how many centimetres is 1m 56cm less than 2m? _____ cm

7. Find the change from a 50p after spending 14p. _____ p

8. Which of these measurements is nearest to 1m?

| 85cm | 93cm | 102cm | 96cm |

_____ cm

9. How many faces has a cone? _____

10. How many times can 3 be taken from 21? _____

C | Answer

1. Find the total cost of two postcards at 7p each and two at 9p each. _____ p

2. What is the smallest whole number that can be divided by both 3 and 4? _____

3. A centimetre square has four equal sides each measuring 1cm. How many centimetre squares could be fitted into this rectangle? _____

16cm

1cm

4. Harry lost 15p, which was $\frac{3}{4}$ of his money. How much had he at first? _____ p

5. An eight-day camping trip started on 25 May. On what date did it end? _____

6. How much change out of two 50ps after paying for $1\frac{1}{2}$ kg of bananas at 64p per kg? _____ p

7. Paper clips are bought at three for 8p. How many for two 20ps? _____

8. How many children had one sister? _____

number of sisters   ☺ = 10 children

3	☺
2	☺ ☺
1	☺ ☺ ☺
0	☺

9. Amelia has 4p, Poppy 11p and Preet 9p. If all their money is shared equally, how much will each person have? _____ p

10. How many vertices in a cuboid? _____

A — Answer

1. $(5 \times 100) + (3 \times 10) =$ _____

2. $6 + 20 + 7 =$ _____

3. $(6 \times 5) + 3 =$ _____

4. $20cm - 5\frac{1}{2}cm =$ _____ cm

5. $240 = 10 + \blacksquare + 200$ _____

6. $\frac{1}{2}kg - 100g = \blacksquare g$ _____ g

7. $\blacksquare \div 5 = 9$ _____

8. $(16cm - 8cm) + 5cm =$ _____ cm

9. $1070g = 1kg \; \blacksquare g$ _____ g

10. $\frac{1}{3}$ of 12 + $\frac{1}{4}$ of 20 = _____

B — Answer

1. What is the next odd number greater than 69? _____

2. From 403 take 10. _____

3. Divide 35cm into 10 equal parts. What is the length of each part? _____ cm

4. What number is added to 8 to make 278? _____

5. How many grams in 1kg 40g? _____ g

6. Write the missing sign +, −, × or ÷ in place of the ●.
   $13 - 5 = 8 \; ● \; 1.$ _____

7. How many centimetres when 37cm is added to $\frac{1}{2}$m? _____ cm

8. $50p + 34p + 20p = £\blacksquare$ £ _____

9. In 56 there are 7 groups of 8. How many groups of 7 are there in 56? _____

10. What is the change from two 20ps after spending 29p? _____ p

C — Answer

1. Write in words the time that is 35 minutes after ten to five. _____

2. Luke does his homework for $1\frac{1}{2}$ hours each day, Monday to Friday. How many hours does he spend on homework per week? _____ h

3. Estimate which two of these lines, W, X, Y and Z, are of equal length. _____

4. 100g of pears cost 20p. Find the cost of $\frac{1}{2}$kg. £ _____

5. What is the total number of days in the first three months of a leap year? _____

6. What is the total cost of four pots of paint at 80p per pot? £ _____

7. A rectangle has

   rectangle

   a ☐ pairs of equal opposite sides   a _____

   b ☐ right angles.   b _____

8. By how much is 48p per metre cheaper than 57p per metre? _____ p

9. A bag of pasta has a mass of 1kg 200g. Write the mass in grams. _____ g

10. Find the total value of these coins. _____ p

A | Answer

1. 400 − 200 − 50 =

2. (7 × 10) + 6 =

3. One-fifth of thirty =

4. ▢ ÷ 8 = 12

5. $2 \times \frac{3}{4}$ =

6. 750g = 500g + ▢ g   _____ g

7. 30p + 60p = £1.00 − ▢ p   _____ p

8. 45p = ▢ 5ps   _____ 5ps

9. $\frac{1}{2}$m + 18cm = ▢ cm   _____ cm

10. 70 + 9 = ▢ + 60

B | Answer

1. What number when multiplied by six gives sixty as the answer?

2. How much is added to three 2ps and one 5p to make 20p?   _____ p

3. To the product of 3 and 6 add 5.

4. What is the difference between the largest and smallest of these numbers?

$1\frac{1}{2}$	$\frac{3}{4}$	4	$3\frac{1}{4}$

5. From £1.15 take 90p.   _____ p

6. What length is 5cm less than $\frac{1}{2}$m?   _____ cm

7. If 32p is divided equally between five children, how many pence are left?   _____ p

8.  How many minutes from the time on the clock to ten to 11?   _____ min

9. Rearrange the numbers 4, 6, 9 to make the largest possible odd number.

10. $\frac{1}{2}$kg is ▢ g less than 625g.   _____ g

C | Answer

1. How many 50p coins make the same value as £3.00?   _____ 50ps

2. Freya's hand span measures 12cm. Find the length of five spans.   _____ cm

3. A glass holds $\frac{1}{2}$l. How many times can it be filled from a bottle holding 8l?

4. In a school there are 523 pupils. If 40 pupils leave, how many remain?

5. Grace has four bank notes of the same value. She has £200. What is the value of each note?   £ _____

6. A chef requires 8kg of oranges. How much money will be saved by ordering the cheaper variety?   _____ p

Oranges 69p per kg	Oranges 73p per kg

7. Tom leaves home at 8 o'clock a.m. and returns at 5 o'clock p.m. For how many hours is he away from home?   _____ h

8. Gulshan gives 68p to her sister. She has four 10ps and two 5ps left. How much had she at first?   £ _____

9. Which of these numbers is a multiple of both 3 and 6?

15	21	30	39

10. The distance round the triangle is 25cm. Two sides each measure 9cm.

   triangle (9cm, 9cm)

   What is the length of the third side?   _____ cm

A — Answer

1. 50 tens + 8 units =

2. 3 + 3 + 3 + 3 + 3 + 3 + 3 + 3 =

3. $\frac{1}{4}$ of 1m = ▢ cm _____ cm

4. £1.00 − 45p = ▢ p _____ p

5. 10 × 0 = 8 × ▢

6. 489 + 20 =

7. $\frac{1}{2}$ kg = 850g − ▢ g _____ g

8. 1 = $\frac{1}{5}$ + ▢

9. How many days in August and September together?

10. 85cm + ▢ cm = 1m _____ cm

B — Answer

1. 5 more than 17 minus 8

2. Add the even numbers between 9 and 15.

3. How many 10ps are worth £2.70? _____ 10ps

4. 8 × 5 = 5 × ▢

5.  What is the time 3 hours before the time on the clock? Use a.m. or p.m.

   afternoon

6. If 36 is divided by a number the answer is 9. What is the number?

7. Find the cost of five toothbrushes at 70p each. £ _____

8. One-tenth of 460

9. From 2m take 75cm. _____ m _____ cm

10. Find the difference between five 5ps and seven 2ps. _____ p

C — Answer

1. How many stickers are there in 12 packets, each containing 20 stickers?

2. Nyasha has 18p, which is $\frac{3}{4}$ of her money. How much is half of her money? _____ p

3. A length of rope measures 1m 24cm. It is cut into two equal pieces. Find the length of each piece. _____ cm

4. By how many grams is parcel B heavier than parcel A? _____ g

5. George's birthday is in October. Mia is 5 months older than George. In which month is her birthday?

6. How much more than £1.00 did Leah spend after paying for 1$\frac{1}{2}$ kg of onions at 40p per $\frac{1}{2}$ kg? _____ p

7. A bath, when full, holds 60l. It is $\frac{1}{4}$ full. How many more litres are required to fill it? _____ l

8. What number is the arrow pointing to?

9. Maisy changes eighteen 1ps and six 2ps for 5ps. How many 5ps did she receive? _____ 5ps

10. Which of these angles, A, B, C or D, is less than a right angle?

A   Answer

1. $614 =$ ☐ tens 4 units   _____ T

2. Half of $(15 - 7) =$ _____

3. $130cm + 70cm =$ ☐ m   _____ m

4. $4\frac{3}{4} =$ ☐ quarters   _____

5. $(6p \times 8) + 2p =$ _____ p

6. $1 - \frac{7}{10} =$ ☐   _____

7. $24 \div 4 = 3 \times$ ☐   _____

8. £1.00 − 16p = ☐ p   _____ p

9. $630 - 50 =$ _____

10. $1kg =$ ☐ g + 750g   _____ g

B   Answer

1. What is the value of the digit underlined in the number 8<u>6</u>3?   _____

2. To 23p add 17p and 5p.   _____ p

3. Write the missing sign $+$, $-$, $\times$ or $\div$ in place of the ●.

   6 tens ● 8 units = 52   _____

4. Decrease £1.35 by 29p.   £ _____

5. What is the missing number in this sequence?

   48, 42, 36, 30, ☐   _____

6. By how many centimetres is 2m more than $\frac{1}{2}$m?   _____ cm

7. How many times can 5 be subtracted from 40?   _____

8. Divide £0.48 by 8. Write the answer in pence.   _____ p

9. How many minutes in $2\frac{1}{2}$ hours?   _____ min

10. $3\overline{)\,\begin{array}{cc}1 & 2\\ \blacksquare & \blacksquare\end{array}}$ _____

C   Answer

1. A piece of tape measures 40cm. Find the length in metres of 10 pieces.   _____ m

2. Oscar practises his recorder for $\frac{3}{4}$ hour. He begins at quarter to twelve a.m. Write in words what time he finishes, using a.m. or p.m.   _____

3. How many yoghurts are bought for £6.00?   _____

Yoghurts
6 for £1.50

4. A side of a square measures $9\frac{1}{2}$ cm. Find the total length of its sides.   _____ cm

5. 1l of water has a mass of 1kg. What is the mass in grams of $\frac{1}{2}$ litre of water?   _____ g

6. £2.38 has the same value as £2, three 10ps and some 2ps. How many 2ps?   _____ 2ps

7. Ahmed measures his folder, which is 50cm long. How many folders measure 7m?   _____

8. A sum of money is divided into two parts. One part is worth 7p and the other is worth three times as much. What is the sum of money?   _____ p

9. The mass of each of three parcels is 420g, $\frac{1}{4}$ kg and 390g. By how many grams is the heaviest parcel greater than the lightest?   _____ g

10. 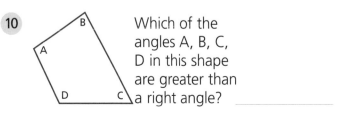 Which of the angles A, B, C, D in this shape are greater than a right angle?   _____

A Write in words the number shown on each abacus.

_____ _____ _____ _____

_____ _____ _____ _____

B Write these numbers in digits.

five hundred	_____
one hundred and sixty-three	_____
four hundred and thirteen	_____
nine hundred and forty	_____
three hundred and five	_____
two hundred and eighty-nine	_____
eight hundred and twenty-four	_____
one hundred and two	_____
seven hundred and seventy	_____
one thousand	_____

C

400 + 60 + 3 =	_____	
700 + 80 =	_____	
600 + 1 =	_____	
300 + 10 + 9 =	_____	
500 + 20 =	_____	
100 + 16 =	_____	
379 = tens 9 units	_____	T
404 = ▢ tens 4 units	_____	T
230 = 2 hundreds units	_____	U
865 = 8 hundreds ▢ units	_____	U

D Addition

7 + 2 =	____	16 + 3 =	____
5 + 5 =	____	2 + 18 =	____
3 + 6 =	____	5 + 14 =	____
0 + 9 =	____	11 + 8 =	____
2 + 8 =	____	7 + 13 =	____
8 + 3 =	____	15 + 7 =	____
5 + 9 =	____	13 + 8 =	____
7 + 4 =	____	5 + 16 =	____
2 + 9 =	____	18 + 4 =	____
4 + 8 =	____	6 + 19 =	____
6 + 5 =	____	17 + 7 =	____
8 + 8 =	____	6 + 14 =	____
7 + 6 =	____	19 + 4 =	____
9 + 9 =	____	5 + 18 =	____
6 + 8 =	____	7 + 19 =	____
6 + 6 =	____	15 + 5 =	____
8 + 5 =	____	29 + 8 =	____
3 + 9 =	____	7 + 26 =	____
8 + 9 =	____	8 + 27 =	____
9 + 6 =	____	4 + 29 =	____

E Subtraction

9 − 5 =	____	17 − 4 =	____
7 − 3 =	____	19 − 6 =	____
8 − 0 =	____	18 − 5 =	____
10 − 4 =	____	14 − 10 =	____
10 − 7 =	____	16 − 6 =	____
12 − 3 =	____	21 − 2 =	____
14 − 5 =	____	22 − 5 =	____
11 − 7 =	____	24 − 7 =	____
13 − 9 =	____	25 − 6 =	____
17 − 9 =	____	26 − 9 =	____
16 − 8 =	____	24 − 6 =	____
13 − 5 =	____	25 − 9 =	____
14 − 9 =	____	22 − 7 =	____
13 − 6 =	____	21 − 6 =	____
14 − 8 =	____	25 − 7 =	____
17 − 8 =	____	21 − 8 =	____
18 − 9 =	____	32 − 9 =	____
15 − 8 =	____	31 − 4 =	____
16 − 7 =	____	34 − 5 =	____
13 − 8 =	____	33 − 7 =	____

A Write the missing number in each of these sequences.

270, 370, 470, 570,   _____

403, 303, 203, 103, ▨ _____

360, 370, 380, 390, ▨ _____

135, 125, 115, 105, ▨ _____

How many times larger is

100 than 10 _____

1000 than 100 _____

300 than 3 _____

460 than 46? _____

Write the value of the digits underlined.

7̲06 _____

85̲0 _____

6̲03 _____

B Addition

20 + 50 = _____

10 + 90 = _____

39 + 40 = _____

70 + 18 = _____

95 + 6 = _____

75 + 30 = _____

92 + 9 = _____

150 + 50 = _____

247 + 100 = _____

180 + 20 = _____

396 + 10 = _____

199 + 1 = _____

298 + 5 = _____

106 + 7 = _____

509 + 4 = _____

C Subtraction

60 − 40 = _____

80 − 50 = _____

47 − 10 = _____

99 − 30 = _____

87 − 17 = _____

32 − 12 = _____

74 − 4 = _____

112 − 10 = _____

208 − 100 = _____

460 − 60 = _____

103 − 6 = _____

300 − 7 = _____

201 − 10 = _____

500 − 40 = _____

310 − 5 = _____

 D Multiplication

2 × 6 = _____   (1 × 5) + 3 = _____

7 × 3 = _____   (3 × 4) + 2 = _____

5 × 4 = _____   (5 × 5) + 2 = _____

8 × 5 = _____   (7 × 10) + 6 = _____

4 × 6 = _____   (9 × 3) + 2 = _____

3 × 10 = _____   (8 × 6) + 5 = _____

0 × 3 = _____   (7 × 4) + 2 = _____

1 × 6 = _____   (9 × 8) + 4 = _____

2 × 5 = _____   (0 × 10) + 5 = _____

10 × 6 = _____   (1 × 8) + 4 = _____

7 × 5 = _____   (2 × 4) + 3 = _____

4 × 8 = _____   (6 × 3) + 2 = _____

6 × 8 = _____   (8 × 2) + 1 = _____

9 × 2 = _____   (5 × 6) + 4 = _____

4 × 9 = _____   (8 × 8) + 5 = _____

E Division

12 ÷ 2 = _____   22 ÷ 2 = _____

15 ÷ 5 = _____   32 ÷ 4 = _____

50 ÷ 10 = _____   100 ÷ 10 = _____

18 ÷ 3 = _____   60 ÷ 5 = _____

40 ÷ 8 = _____   33 ÷ 3 = _____

24 ÷ 4 = _____   96 ÷ 8 = _____

0 ÷ 3 = _____   120 ÷ 10 = _____

35 ÷ 5 = _____   8 ÷ 8 = _____

56 ÷ 8 = _____   0 ÷ 3 = _____

16 ÷ 2 = _____   48 ÷ 4 = _____

32 ÷ 4 = _____   88 ÷ 8 = _____

70 ÷ 10 = _____   110 ÷ 10 = _____

0 ÷ 5 = _____   44 ÷ 4 = _____

21 ÷ 3 = _____   10 ÷ 10 = _____

48 ÷ 8 = _____   36 ÷ 3 = _____

F Find the total of 9, 7, 4 and 2. _____

29 minus 10 = _____

8 times 3 = _____

Increase 15 by 9. _____

Divide 36 into 4 equal parts. _____

What is the difference between 8 and 23? _____

Find the product of 9 and 10. _____

What number is added to 16 to make 25? _____

By how many is 18 less than 26? _____

What number when multiplied by 8 gives 56 as the answer? _____

A

10p =
- ☐ 5ps _____
- ☐ 2ps

20p =
- ☐ 10ps _____
- ☐ 5ps
- ☐ 2ps

50p =
- ☐ 10ps _____
- ☐ 5ps
- ☐ 2ps

£1 =
- ☐ 50ps _____
- ☐ 20ps _____
- ☐ 10ps _____
- ☐ 5ps _____
- ☐ 2ps _____
- ☐ 1ps _____

B Find the total value of the coins in each row.

  _____ p

seven 10ps = _____ p

    _____ p

eight 5ps = _____ p

twelve 2ps = _____ p

   _____ p

two 10ps and three 2ps = _____ p

four 2ps and 5p = _____ p

 £ _____

four 10ps and six 5ps = _____ p

one 50p and two 20ps = _____ p

C

Find the change from a 10p after spending these amounts.	Find the change from a 20p after spending these amounts.	Find the change from a 50p after spending these amounts.	Find the change from £1 after spending these amounts.
4p _____ p	16p _____ p	44p _____ p	93p _____ p
8p _____ p	12p _____ p	38p _____ p	85p _____ p
6p _____ p	14p _____ p	22p _____ p	78p _____ p
2p _____ p	18p _____ p	19p _____ p	61p _____ p
5p _____ p	15p _____ p	36p _____ p	54p _____ p
3p _____ p	11p _____ p	25p _____ p	42p _____ p
1p _____ p	7p _____ p	14p _____ p	36p _____ p
7p _____ p	3p _____ p	9p _____ p	19p _____ p

D Write the missing number of coins.

six 2ps and three 1ps = ☐ 5ps _____

two 10ps and five 2ps = ☐ 5ps _____

one 50p and three 10ps = ☐ 20ps _____

one 50p and two 20ps = ☐ 10ps _____

£1 is worth

four 20ps and ☐ 10ps _____

one 50p and ☐ 10ps _____

one 50p, one 20p and ☐ 10ps _____

one 50p, two 20ps and ☐ 5ps _____

CHECK-UP TEST | Measurement

A

V ——————————————————————————————————

  W ————————————————————————————————

    X ———————————————————————————

  Y ————————————————————————————————

    Z ————————————————————————

Without using a ruler, estimate which of the lines V, W, X, Y, Z

is the longest _____

is the shortest _____

are of equal length _____

measures 9cm _____

measures 14cm. _____

B Write the missing numbers.

10mm	= ▢ cm	_____ cm	1m 35cm	= ▢ cm	_____ cm
25 half-cm	= ▢ cm	_____ cm	$\frac{1}{2}$m − 40cm	= ▢ cm	_____ cm
1m	= ▢ cm	_____ cm	2m + ▢ cm	= 265cm	_____ cm
$\frac{1}{2}$m	= ▢ cm	_____ cm	$\frac{1}{2}$m + 90cm	= ▢ cm	_____ cm
$\frac{1}{4}$m	= ▢ cm	_____ cm	54cm + ▢ cm	= 1m	_____ cm
$\frac{3}{4}$m	= ▢ cm	_____ cm	$\frac{1}{4}$m + 150cm	= ▢ m	_____ m
1kg	= ▢ g	_____ g	1kg − 750g	= ▢ g	_____ g
$\frac{1}{2}$kg	= ▢ g	_____ g	$\frac{1}{2}$kg + ▢ g	= 700g	_____ g
$\frac{1}{10}$kg	= ▢ g	_____ g	2kg 400g	= ▢ g	_____ g
1 litre	= ▢ ml	_____ ml	250g + 250g	= ▢ kg	_____ kg

C Write the time shown on each clock face in words using a.m. or p.m.

morning

afternoon

morning

afternoon

_____

D

			How many days in		How long is it from 10 o'clock a.m. to		
1h	= ▢ min	_____	April	_____	midday	_____ h	_____ min
$\frac{1}{2}$h	= ▢ min	_____	July	_____	1 o'clock p.m.	_____ h	_____ min
$\frac{1}{4}$h	= ▢ min	_____	January	_____	half past four p.m.	_____ h	_____ min
$\frac{3}{4}$h	= ▢ min	_____	October	_____	ten to six p.m.	_____ h	_____ min
1 week	= ▢ days	_____	June?	_____	ten past ten p.m.?	_____ h	_____ min
1 year	= ▢ months	_____					

47

Schofield & Sims

the long-established educational publisher specialising in maths, English and science

Mental Arithmetic provides rich and varied practice to meet the requirements of the National Curriculum for primary mathematics. Questions in **Mental Arithmetic 1** cover the key subject areas of number, measurement, geometry and statistics, including place value, simple fractions, times tables, telling the time, giving change, and 2-D and 3-D shapes. The accompanying answer book, **Mental Arithmetic 1 Answers**, contains answers to all the questions included in **Mental Arithmetic 1**.

Mental Arithmetic comprises seven one-per-child pupil books with accompanying answer books, as well as a single Teacher's Guide. The series develops pupils' essential maths skills, preparing them for the Key Stage 2 national tests. It may also be used as preparation for the 11+, and with older students for consolidation and recovery. All the books can be used flexibly for individual, paired, group or whole-class maths practice, as well as for homework and one-to-one intervention.

Structured according to ability rather than age, the series allows children to work at their own pace, building confidence and fluency. Two **Entry Tests** are available in the **Mental Arithmetic Teacher's Guide** and on the Schofield & Sims website, enabling teachers, parents and tutors to select the appropriate book for each child.

Mental Arithmetic 1 contains:
- 36 one-page tests, each comprising the following three parts
    Part A: questions where use of language is kept to a minimum
    Part B: questions using number vocabulary
    Part C: questions focusing on one- and two-step word problems
- **Progress Tests** to monitor learning as pupils work through the book
- **Check-up Tests** to identify any gaps in understanding.

Mental Arithmetic
  Introductory Book
	978 07217 0798 3	**Mental Arithmetic**
		  Introductory Book Answers
			978 07217 0853 9

Mental Arithmetic 1	978 07217 0799 0	**Mental Arithmetic 1 Answers**	978 07217 0805 8
Mental Arithmetic 2	978 07217 0800 3	**Mental Arithmetic 2 Answers**	978 07217 0806 5
Mental Arithmetic 3	978 07217 0801 0	**Mental Arithmetic 3 Answers**	978 07217 0807 2
Mental Arithmetic 4	978 07217 0802 7	**Mental Arithmetic 4 Answers**	978 07217 0808 9
Mental Arithmetic 5	978 07217 0803 4	**Mental Arithmetic 5 Answers**	978 07217 0809 6
Mental Arithmetic 6	978 07217 0804 1	**Mental Arithmetic 6 Answers**	978 07217 0810 2
Mental Arithmetic **Teacher's Guide**	978 07217 1389 2		

First Mental Arithmetic is available for younger pupils

This edition copyright © Schofield & Sims Ltd, 2016. Twelfth impression 2019.
First edition published in 1976, compiled by J W Adams and R P Beaumont, edited by T R Goddard.
British Library Cataloguing in Publication Data. A catalogue record for this book is available from the British Library.
All rights reserved. Except where otherwise indicated, no part of this publication may be reproduced, stored in a retrieval system, or transmitted in any form or by any means, electronic, mechanical, photocopying, recording or otherwise, without either the prior permission of the publisher or a licence permitting restricted copying in the United Kingdom issued by the Copyright Licensing Agency Limited.
Design by Ledgard Jepson Ltd. Front cover design by Peter Grundy. Printed in the UK by Page Bros (Norwich) Ltd.

Mental Arithmetic

MIX
Paper from responsible sources
FSC® C023114

ISBN 978-07217-0799-0

9 780721 707990

For further information and to place your order visit
www.schofieldandsims.co.uk or telephone 01484 607080

ISBN 978 07217 0799 0
Key Stage 2
Age range 7–11+ years
£3.95 (Retail price)